Zaner-Bloser
Handwriting

jump

ZB **Zaner-Bloser**

Senior Consultant

Steve Graham, Ed.D., Currey Ingram Professor of Special Education and Literacy, Vanderbilt University

Occupational Therapy Consultants

Jane Case-Smith, Ed.D., OTR/L, FAOTA, Chair of the Occupational Therapy Division, Ohio State University

Mary Benbow, M.S., OTR, La Jolla, CA

Asha Asher, MA OTR/L, FAOTA, M.Ed. (Special Education), Cincinnati, OH
North Shore Pediatric Therapy

ELL Consultants

Ellen Riojas Clark, Ph.D., Professor of Bicultural-Bilingual Studies, University of Texas at San Antonio

Bertha Pérez, Ed.D., Professor Emeritus of Literacy, University of Texas at San Antonio

Consultant

Debbie Diller, Educational Consultant, Houston, TX

Occupational Therapy Advisory Board

Kathleen A. Benton-Sanchez, M.P.A., OTR/L, Nashville, TN
Sherry Eisenbach, OT/L, Portland, OR
Elizabeth Gerich, OTR/L, Plymouth, MN
Sheila Martins, OTR/L, North Las Vegas, NV

Carol Miller, OTR/L, Marietta, OH
Leslie N. Parker, OTR/L, Huntington, WV
Tricia Shibuya, OTR/L, Las Vegas, NV
Denaysa Sisemore, M.S., OTR/L, Windsor, CO
Cheryl Weaver, CAS, M.S.Ed., OTR/L, Macedon, NY

Reviewers

Amy Bass, National Heritage Academies, Byron Center, MI
Donetta S. Brown, Birmingham City Schools, AL
Kelly Caravelli, Poway Unified School District, San Diego, CA
Michelle Corsi, East Windsor Regional Schools, NJ
Naomi Drewitz, East Windsor Regional Schools, NJ
Shan Glandon, Tulsa, OK
Karen Jackson, School District of Philadelphia, PA
Liz Knowles, Ed.D., 21st Century Curriculum Designs, LLC, Del Ray Beach, FL
Rita Olsen, Chicago Public Schools, IL
Geraldine A. Pappas, Detroit Public Schools, MI
Michael E. Pizzingrillo, Roman Catholic Diocese of Brooklyn, NY
Deborah C. Thomas, Ed.D., Montgomery Public Schools, AL
Ellen Lerch Thomsen, Roanoke County Public Schools, VA
Iefay Williams, School District of Philadelphia, PA

SUSTAINABLE FORESTRY INITIATIVE

Certified Sourcing
www.sfiprogram.org
SFI-01042

CONTENTS

Your Book
Models and Guidelines

There are writing models in your book. The models are on guidelines. The red arrows and numerals show you how to write each letter.

Start at the green dot when you trace and write.

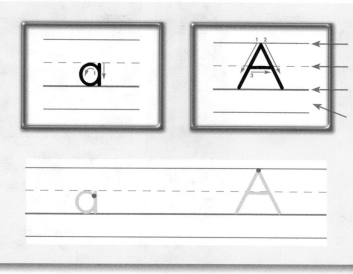

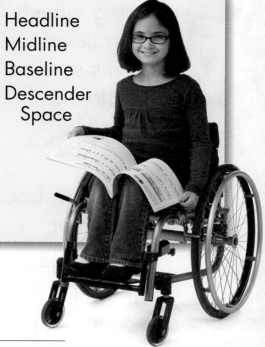

Headline
Midline
Baseline
Descender
Space

Stop and Check

When you see a **Stop and Check** sign, circle the best letter you wrote on that line.

Circle the best letter on this line.

a a a a

Keys to Legibility

There are four kinds of keys in your book.
The words on the keys are **Shape, Size, Spacing,** and **Slant**.

Good writers think about these things when they write.
The Keys will help you make your writing legible.
Legible means easy to read.

5

Seasons Afoot

Spring wheels in
On roller skates,
Zooms up and down
The street.

Winter plods in
Heavily
With snow-boots
On its feet.

Summer jumps in
Barefoot,
Kicking water
In the pool.

Autumn squeaks
In brand-new shoes—
Nervously, to
School.

Beverly McLoughland

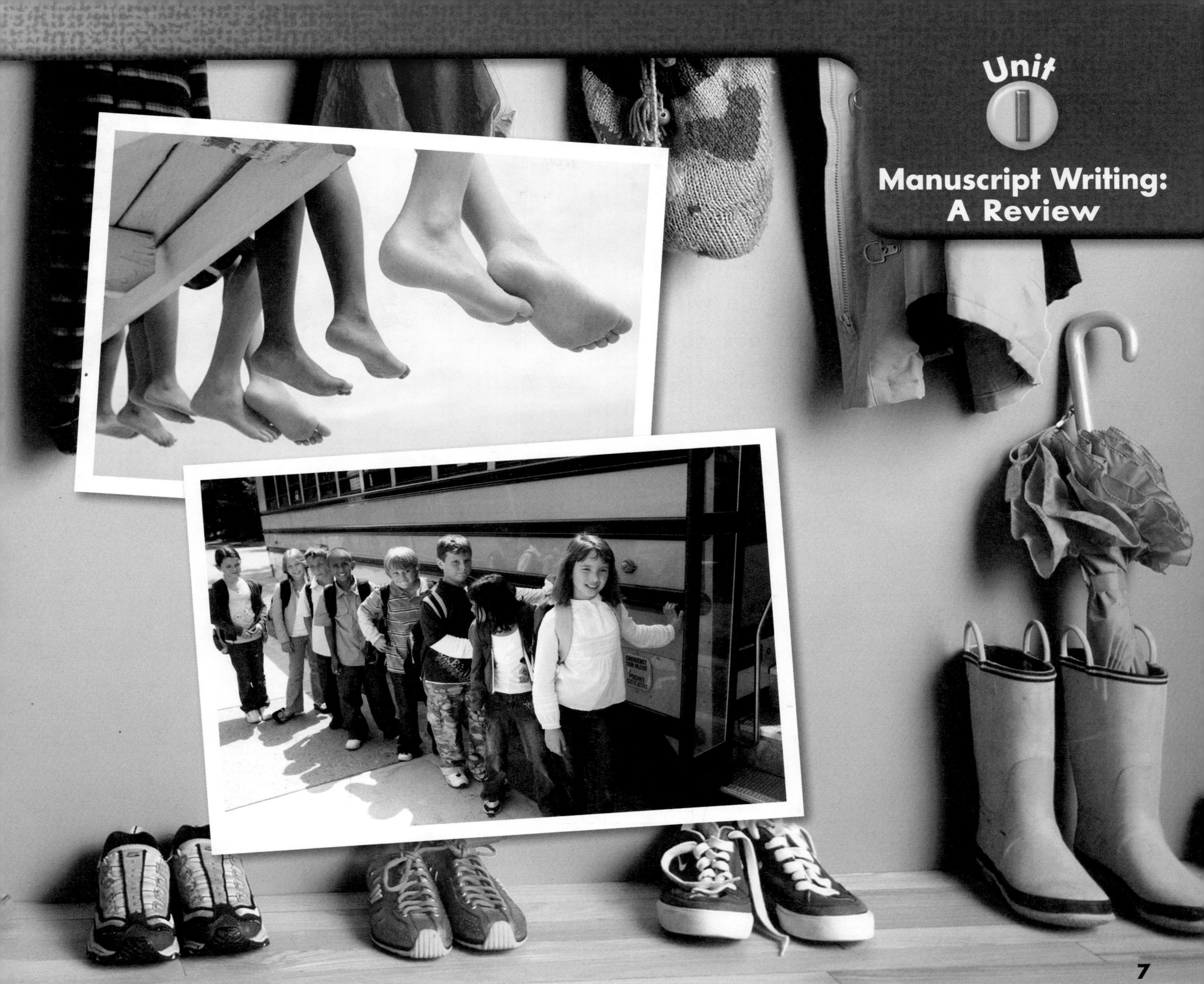

Unit 1
Manuscript Writing: A Review

Show What You Can Do

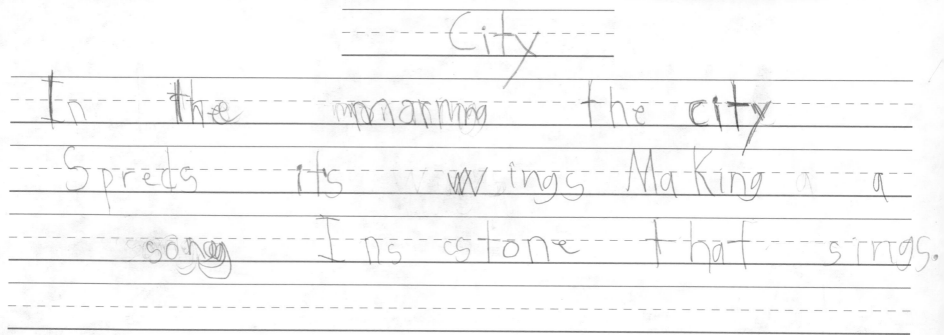

City
In the morning the city
Spreads its wings
Making a song
In stone that sings.

Write the title and the first four lines of the poem.

City

In the morning the city
Spreds its wings Making a a
song Ins stone that sings.

In the evening the city
Goes to bed
Hanging lights
About its head.

by Langston Hughes

Write the next four lines here.

In the evening the city
Goes to bed Hanging lights
about its head by
Langstom Hughes.

If you write with your **LEFT** hand . . .

Sit like this.
Sit comfortably. Lean forward a little.
Keep your feet flat on the floor.

Place the paper like this.

Slant the paper as shown in the picture.

Rest both arms on the desk. Use your right hand to move the paper as you write.

Pull the pencil toward your left elbow when you write.

Hold the pencil like this.

Hold the pencil with your thumb and first two fingers.

Do not squeeze the pencil when you write.

If you write with your **RIGHT** hand . . .

Sit like this.
Sit comfortably. Lean forward a little.
Keep your feet flat on the floor.

Place the paper like this.

Place the paper straight in front of you.

Rest both arms on the desk. Use your left hand to move the paper as you write.

Pull the pencil toward the middle of your body when you write.

Hold the pencil like this.

Hold the pencil with your thumb and first two fingers.

Do not squeeze the pencil when you write.

Vertical Lines

Some letters and numerals have lines that are straight up and down.
Trace the straight up and down lines in each letter and numeral.

| b   i   p   h   T   E   L   5   4

Trace and write these letters and numerals that have vertical lines. Start at the green dot.

t   d   h   j   B   D   F   H   9   I

Horizontal Lines

Some letters and numerals have lines that slide right or slide left.
Trace the slide lines in each letter and numeral.

f   t   e   H   J   G   Z   5   2

Trace and write these letters and numerals that have horizontal lines. Start at the green dot.

e   t   f   z   A   G   F   I   5

Circle Lines

Some letters and numerals have forward circle or backward circle lines.
Trace the circle or part of the circle in each letter and numeral.

c e g C O b p 2 3

Trace and write these letters and numerals that have circle lines. Start at the green dot.

a d f o C B P 3 8

Slant Lines

Some letters and numerals have lines that slant left or slant right.
Trace the slant lines in each letter and numeral.

x z k v W Q A X 7

Trace and write these letters and numerals that have slant lines. Start at the green dot.

w y z V X Q Y Z K 7

Slant

Spacing

Size

Shape

Make your writing easy to read.

Shape

Letters with good shape are easy to read. Trace these letters.

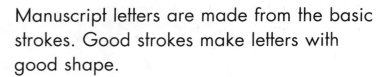

Manuscript letters are made from the basic strokes. Good strokes make letters with good shape.

✔ Circle a letter that has a vertical line (|).

✔ Underline a letter that has a horizontal line (—).

✔ Draw a box around a letter that has a circle line (o c ɔ).

✔ Draw a star beside a letter that has a slant line (\ /).

Size

Letters with good size are easy to read. Trace these letters.

Manuscript letters have two sizes.

Tall letters touch the headline.

Short letters touch the midline.

Some short letters have descenders that go below the baseline and touch the next line.

✔ Circle a short letter.

✔ Underline a tall letter.

✔ Draw a box around a short letter that has a descender.

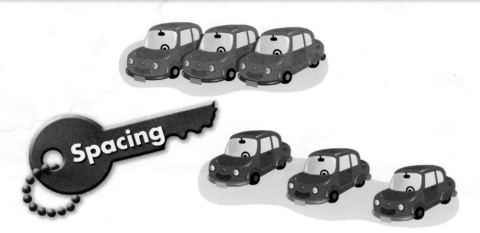

Spacing

Words and letters with good spacing are easy to read. Trace these words.

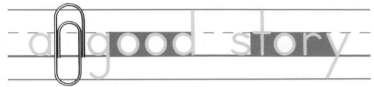

a good story

Look at the spacing between letters. The letters are neither too close together nor too far apart.

Look at the spacing between words. There is enough space for your little finger or a paper clip between words.

✔ Use a paper clip or your little finger to measure the spacing between the words above.

Slant

Letters with good slant are easy to read. Trace these words.

my letters

Look at the vertical slant of the letters. Manuscript letters are straight up and down.

To write with good slant:

1. Place your paper correctly.

2. Pull down in the proper direction.

3. Shift your paper as you write.

✔ Draw lines through the vertical strokes in the letters above. Are all your lines straight up and down?

Trace and write.

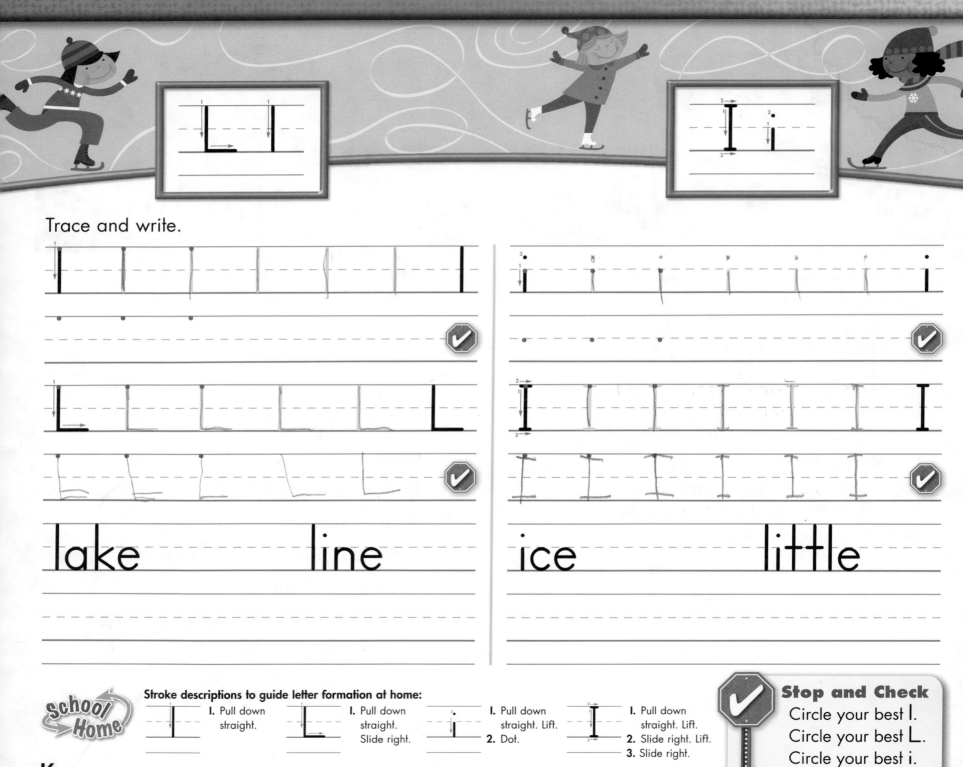

lake   line   ice   little

School Home

Stroke descriptions to guide letter formation at home:

I. Pull down straight.

I. Pull down straight. Slide right.

I. Pull down straight. Lift.
2. Dot.

I. Pull down straight. Lift.
2. Slide right. Lift.
3. Slide right.

Stop and Check
Circle your best I.
Circle your best L.
Circle your best i.
Circle your best I.

Write the words and sentences.

winter   cold   chilly   shiver

Look! I learned to ice-skate.

I can glide and spin.

My Own Writing Write a sentence about something you like to do.

Shape

Circle your best letter that has a vertical line.

Trace and write.

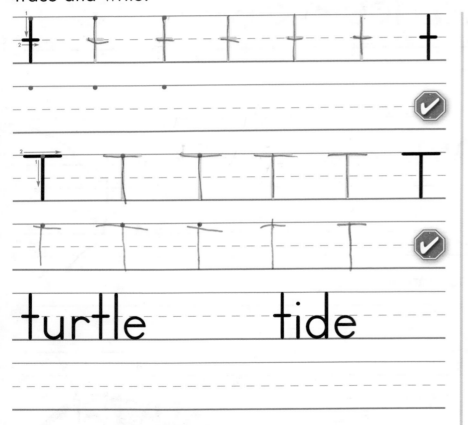

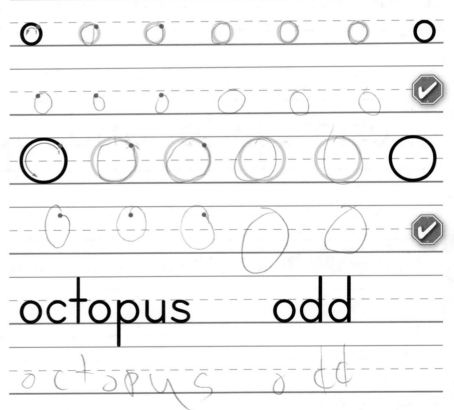

turtle   tide

octopus   odd

octopus odd

School Home

Stroke descriptions to guide letter formation at home:

 1. Pull down straight. Lift.
2. Slide right.

 1. Pull down straight. Lift.
2. Slide right.

1. Circle back all the way around.

 1. Circle back all the way around.

Stop and Check

Circle your best t.
Circle your best T.
Circle your best o.
Circle your best O.

Write the words and sentences.

saltwater   float   otters

Oceans are filled with animals.

The sea is also home to plants.

My Own Writing   Write a sentence about an animal that lives in the ocean.

Size

Circle your
best tall letter.

Trace and write.

a a a a a a a a

A A A A A A

all   page

d d d d d d d

D D D D D D

days   date

Stroke descriptions to guide letter formation at home:

a   1. Circle back all the way around; push up straight. Pull down straight.

A   1. Slant left. Lift.
2. Slant right. Lift.
3. Slide right.

d   1. Circle back all the way around; push up straight. Pull down straight.

D   1. Pull down straight. Lift.
2. Slide right; curve forward; slide left.

20

Stop and Check

Circle your best a.
Circle your best A.
Circle your best d.
Circle your best D.

Write the words and sentences.

a year   seasons   holiday

A calendar shows the months.

December is the last month.

My Own Writing   Write a sentence about your favorite month.

21

Trace and write.

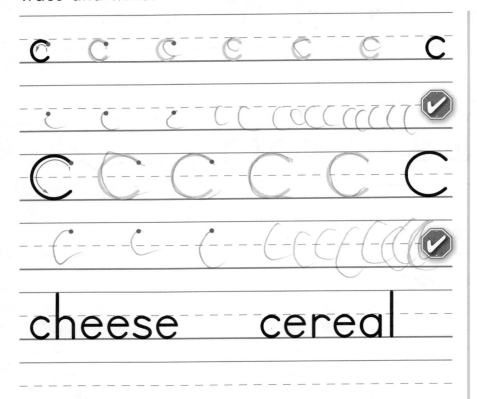

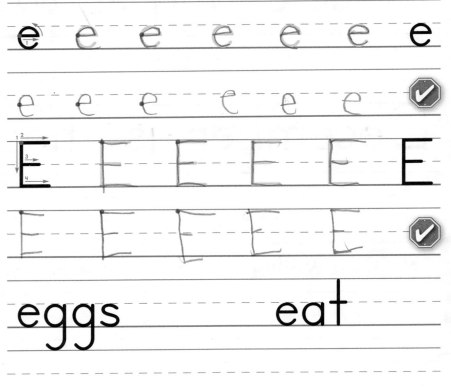

cheese   cereal

eggs   eat

Stroke descriptions to guide letter formation at home:

 c   1. Circle back.

C   1. Circle back.

 e   1. Slide right.
Circle back.

E   1. Pull down
straight. Lift.
2. Slide right. Lift.
3. Slide right; stop
short. Lift.
4. Slide right.

Stop and Check
Circle your best **c**.
Circle your best **C**.
Circle your best **e**.
Circle your best **E**.

Write the words and sentences.

cherries   bread   carrots

Eat good food every day.

Choose healthy meals.

My Own Writing   Write a sentence about your favorite meal.

Circle a word that has good vertical slant.

Trace and write.

f f f f f f f f f

F F F F F F F

fence   farm

g g g g g g g

G G G G G G G

garden   green

Stroke descriptions to guide letter formation at home:

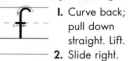 f
1. Curve back; pull down straight. Lift.
2. Slide right.

 F
1. Pull down straight. Lift.
2. Slide right. Lift.
3. Slide right; stop short.

g
1. Circle back all the way around; push up straight. Pull down straight; curve back.

 G
1. Circle back. Slide left.

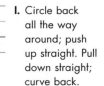 **Stop and Check**

Circle your best f.
Circle your best F.
Circle your best g.
Circle your best G.

24

Write the words and sentences.

feed   ground   fancy   growing

Flowers grow in my garden.

Growing tomatoes is fun.

My Own Writing   Write a sentence that tells what plants need to grow.

Shape

Circle your best letter that has a circle line.

25

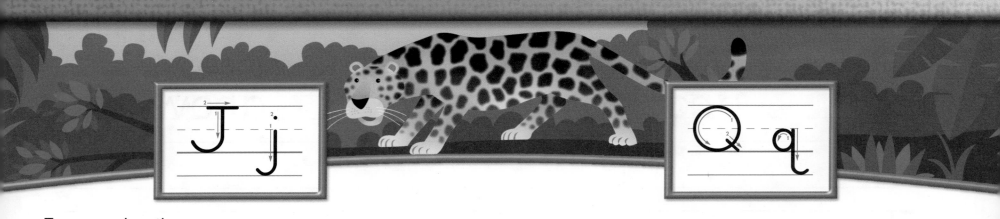

Trace and write.

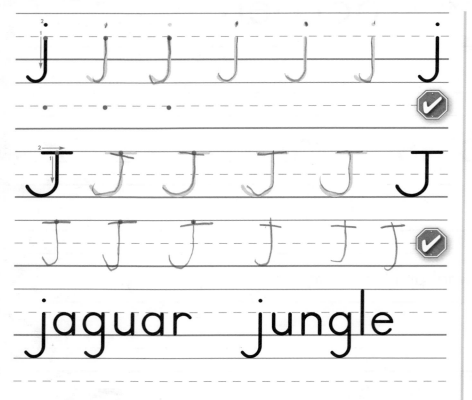

j j j j j j j j j

J J J J J J J

q q q q q q q q

q q q q q q

Q Q Q Q Q Q

jaguar   jungle

quick   quiet

Stroke descriptions to guide letter formation at home:

 1. Pull down straight; curve back. Lift.
2. Dot.

 1. Pull down straight; curve back. Lift.
2. Slide right.

 1. Circle back all the way around; push up straight. Pull down straight; curve forward.

Q 1. Circle back all the way around. Lift.
2. Slant right.

Stop and Check

Circle your best j.

Circle your best J.

Circle your best q.

Circle your best Q.

Write the words and sentences.

just   jolt   quite   join

Jaguars are such quick animals.

Quickly, they jump and pounce.

My Own Writing Write a fact about a wild animal.

27

Trace and write.

u u u u u u u u u u

U U U U U U U U U U

under   up

s s s s s s s s s

S S S S S S S S

sunset   shine

School Home

Stroke descriptions to guide letter formation at home:

u — I. Pull down straight; curve forward; push up. Pull down straight.

U — I. Pull down straight; curve forward; push up.

s — I. Curve back; curve forward.

S — I. Curve back; curve forward.

Stop and Check

Circle your best u.
Circle your best U.
Circle your best s.
Circle your best S.

Write the words and sentences.

sparkle   clouds   sunlight

Usually, I see many stars.

Stars twinkle in the sky.

My Own Writing Write a sentence about what you see in the sky.

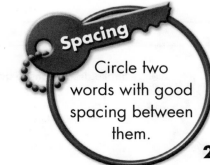

Spacing

Circle two words with good spacing between them.

B b   P p

Trace and write.

b b b b b b b

p p p p p p p

B B B B B B

P P P P P P

baseball   bat

pitcher   plate

School Home

Stroke descriptions to guide letter formation at home:

b   l. Pull down straight. Push up; circle forward.

B   l. Pull down straight. Lift.
2. Slide right; curve forward; slide left. Slide right; curve forward; slide left.

p   l. Pull down straight. Push up; circle forward.

P   l. Pull down straight. Lift.
2. Slide right; curve forward; slide left.

Stop and Check
Circle your best b.
Circle your best B.
Circle your best p.
Circle your best P.

Write the words and sentences.

ball game   bases   playing

Baseball is my best sport.

Pitching is easy for me.

My Own Writing   Write a sentence about a sport you like.

Slant

Circle a word that has good vertical slant.

31

Trace and write.

r r r r r r r r ✓

n n n n n n n ✓

R R R R R R ✓

N N N N N N ✓

rainbow   ray

nature   nice

Stroke descriptions to guide letter formation at home:

r — 1. Pull down straight. Push up; curve forward.

R — 1. Pull down straight. Lift.
2. Slide right; curve forward; slide left. Slant right.

n — 1. Pull down straight. Push up; curve forward; pull down straight.

N — 1. Pull down straight. Lift.
2. Slant right. Push up straight.

32

Stop and Check
Circle your best r.
Circle your best R.
Circle your best n.
Circle your best N.

Write the words and sentences.

red   orange   indigo   green

Rainbows have seven colors.

Name all the colors in order.

My Own Writing Write a sentence about rainbows.

ZB

Shape

Circle your best letter that has a slant line.

Trace and write.

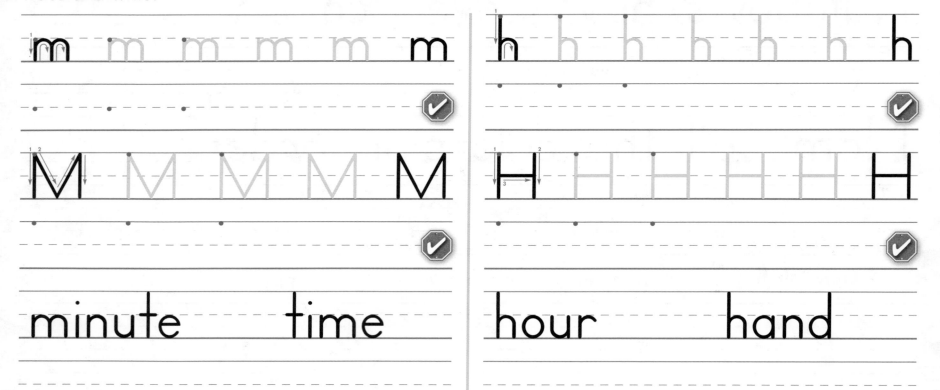

m m m m m m

h h h h h h h

M M M M M

H H H H H H

minute   time

hour   hand

Stroke descriptions to guide letter formation at home:

m
1. Pull down straight. Push up; curve forward; pull down straight. Push up; curve forward; pull down straight.

M
1. Pull down straight. Lift.
2. Slant right. Slant up. Pull down straight.

h
1. Pull down straight. Push up; curve forward; pull down straight.

H
1. Pull down straight. Lift.
2. Pull down straight. Lift.
3. Slide right.

Stop and Check
Circle your best m.
Circle your best M.
Circle your best h.
Circle your best H.

Write the words and sentences.

watch   number   morning   night

My clock has three hands.

Hour hands move slowly.

My Own Writing   Write a sentence about your favorite time of day.

Size

Circle your best short letter.

35

Trace and write.

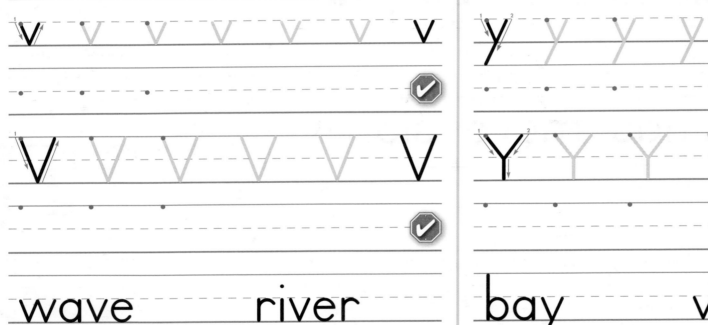

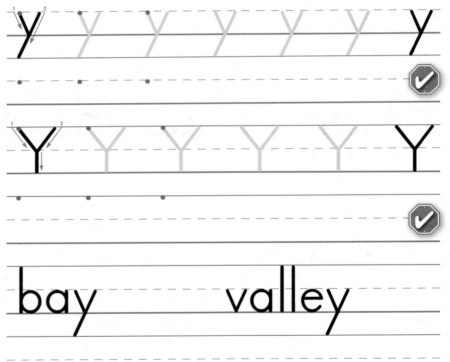

wave   river   bay   valley

Stroke descriptions to guide letter formation at home:

I. Slant right.
   Slant up.

I. Slant right.
   Slant up.

I. Slant right.
   Lift.
2. Slant left.

I. Slant right. Lift.
2. Slant left. Pull
   down straight.

Stop and Check

Circle your best v.

Circle your best V.

Circle your best y.

Circle your best Y.

Write the words and sentences.

very   leaves   yellow   pretty

Visit our nation's parks.

Yosemite is one you will enjoy.

My Own Writing   Write a sentence about a park you have visited.

ZB

Spacing

Circle two letters with good spacing between them.

Trace and write.

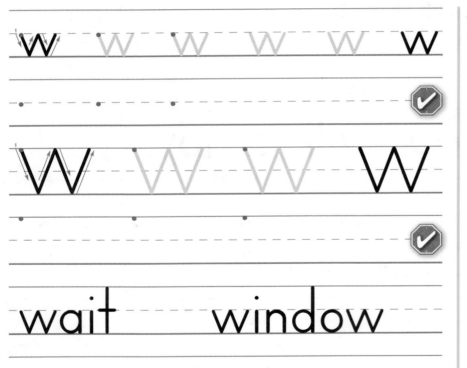

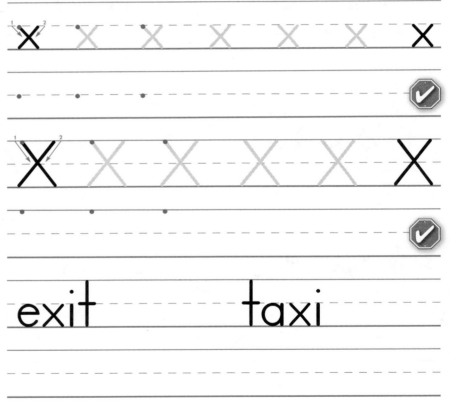

wait   window   exit   taxi

Stroke descriptions to guide letter formation at home:

 I. Slant right.
Slant up.
Slant right.
Slant up.

 I. Slant right.
Slant up.
Slant right.
Slant up.

 I. Slant right.
Lift.
2. Slant left.

I. Slant right. Lift.
2. Slant left.

Stop and Check
Circle your best w.
Circle your best W.
Circle your best x.
Circle your best X.

Write the words and sentences.

highway   excellent   wheel

It's exciting to ride in a taxi.

We go to places in the city.

My Own Writing Write a sentence about a city you would like to visit.

Slant

Circle a word that has good vertical slant.

39

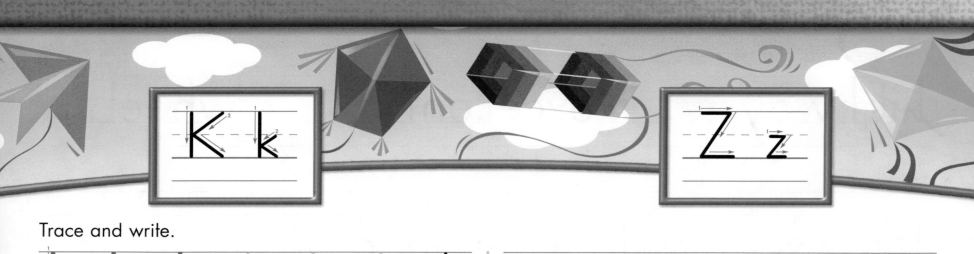

Trace and write.

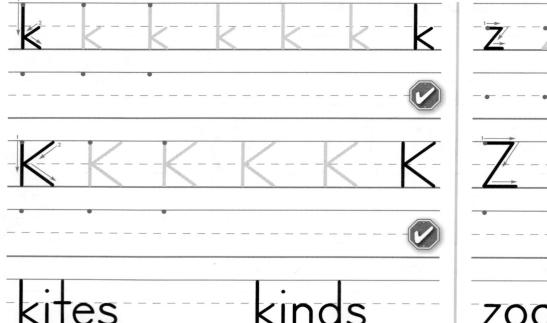 

kites   kinds

zoom   breeze

Stroke descriptions to guide letter formation at home:

k
1. Pull down straight. Lift.
2. Slant left. Slant right.

K
1. Pull down straight. Lift.
2. Slant left. Slant right.

z
1. Slide right. Slant left. Slide right.

Z
1. Slide right. Slant left. Slide right.

Stop and Check
Circle your best k.
Circle your best K.
Circle your best z.
Circle your best Z.

Write the words and sentences.

like   dozen   park   prize

Kites come in all sizes.

Zoom! The big kites fly high.

My Own Writing Write a sentence about something that flies.

Shape

Circle your best letter that has a horizontal line.

41

Writing Numerals

Trace and write.

one | 1 1 1 1

four | 4 4 4 4

two | 2 2 2 2

five | 5 5 5 5

three | 3 3 3 3

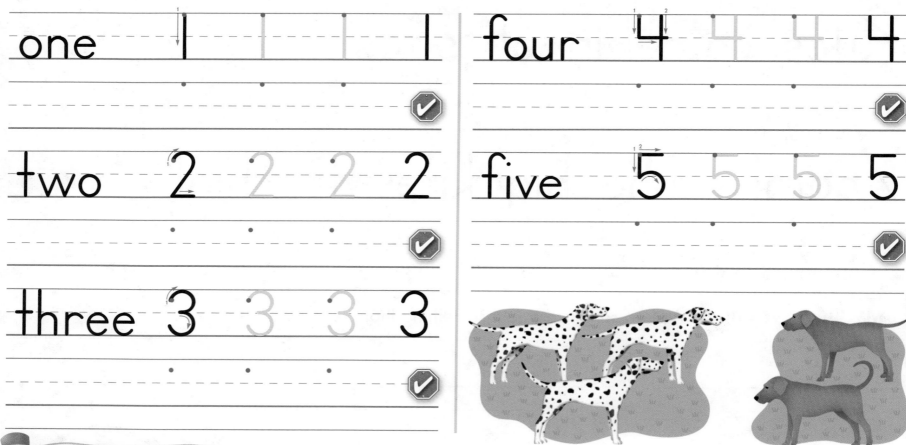

 **My Own Writing** Write a number sentence. Use the plus sign (+) and the equal sign (=).

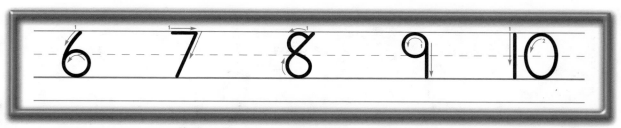

Trace and write.

six 6 6 6 6

seven 7 7 7 7

eight 8 8 8 8

nine 9 9 9 9

ten 10 10 10 10

My Own Writing Write a number sentence. Use the minus sign (–) and the equal sign (=).

Manuscript

City
In the morning the city
Spreads its wings
Making a song
In stone that sings.

Write the first four lines of the poem in your best manuscript handwriting.

44

In the evening the city
Goes to bed
Hanging lights
About its head.

by Langston Hughes

Write the last four lines of the poem in your best manuscript handwriting.

My writing has good Shape. ❑
My writing has good Size. ❑
My writing has good Spacing. ❑
My writing has good Slant. ❑

Only My Opinion

Is a caterpillar ticklish?
Well, it's always my belief
That he giggles as he wiggles
Across a hairy leaf.

Monica Shannon

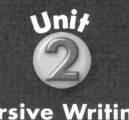

Welcome to Cursive

You are writing very well.
Your manuscript letters look good.
Each letter stands straight up and down,
The way manuscript letters should.

You're ready to write a new way.
You're ready to learn cursive, at last!
Cursive writing is graceful.
Cursive writing is fast.

You are ready for cursive writing! As you begin, you will notice how cursive writing is different from manuscript writing. Look at these words.

ready   *ready*

Notice that the letters in the cursive word are joined together.
Cursive writing slants forward. Write some letters you know in cursive.

What else can you write in cursive? Write it here.

The pages in this book will help you learn to write cursive letters, words, and sentences.

Let's go!

Cursive Letters and Numerals

Circle the uppercase cursive letters that are your initials.
Underline the lowercase cursive letters that are in your name.

Aa Bb Cc Dd Ee Ff Gg

Aa Bb Cc Dd Ee Ff Gg

Hh Ii Jj Kk Ll Mm

Hh Ii Jj Kk Ll Mm

Nn Oo Pp Qq Rr Ss Tt

Nn Oo Pp Qq Rr Ss Tt

Uu Vv Ww Xx Yy Zz

Uu Vv Ww Xx Yy Zz

Circle the cursive numeral that tells your age.

1 2 3 4 5 6 7 8 9 10

1 2 3 4 5 6 7 8 9 10

Reading Cursive Writing

Good morning, my friend.
Good day to you, too.
Where are you going?
What will you do?

Good morning, my friend.
Good day to you, too.
Where are you going?
What will you do?

Read each word in cursive.
Circle the matching word written in manuscript.

friend	boy	friend	girl
day	day	dog	play
you	yes	my	you
do	do	look	go

There are places to go.
There are things to see.
Would you like to follow?
Come along with me.

There are places to go.
There are things to see.
Would you like to follow?
Come along with me.

Read each word in cursive.
Write each word in manuscript.

places _____

things _____

you _____

to _____

go _____

follow _____

like _____

me _____

53

Cursive

If you write with your LEFT hand . . .

Sit like this.

Sit comfortably. Lean forward a little.
Keep your feet flat on the floor.

Place the paper like this.

Slant the paper as shown in the picture.

Rest both arms on the desk. Use your right hand to move the paper as you write.

Pull the pencil toward your left elbow when you write.

Hold the pencil like this.

Hold the pencil with your thumb and first two fingers.

Do not squeeze the pencil when you write.

If you write with your **RIGHT** hand . . .

Sit like this.

Sit comfortably. Lean forward a little.
Keep your feet flat on the floor.

Place the paper like this.

Slant the paper as shown in the picture.

Rest both arms on the desk. Use your left hand to move the paper as you write.

Pull the pencil toward the middle of your body when you write.

Hold the pencil like this.

Hold the pencil with your thumb and first two fingers.

Do not squeeze the pencil when you write.

Basic Strokes

Undercurve

An **undercurve** is one of the basic strokes used to write cursive letters.

An undercurve stroke swings up.

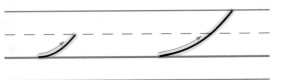

Trace an undercurve stroke at the beginning of each lowercase letter.

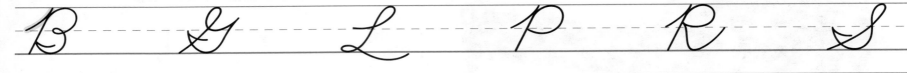

Trace an undercurve stroke at the beginning of each uppercase letter.

Trace and write undercurve strokes.

Downcurve

A **downcurve** is one of the basic strokes used to write cursive letters.

A downcurve stroke dives down.

Trace a downcurve stroke at the beginning of each lowercase letter.

a   c   d   g   o   q

Trace a downcurve stroke in each uppercase letter.

a   C   D   E   O

Trace and write downcurve strokes.

Overcurve

An **overcurve** is one of the basic strokes used to write cursive letters.

An overcurve stroke bounces up.

Trace an overcurve stroke at the beginning of each lowercase letter.

Trace an overcurve stroke at the beginning of each uppercase letter.

Trace and write overcurve strokes.

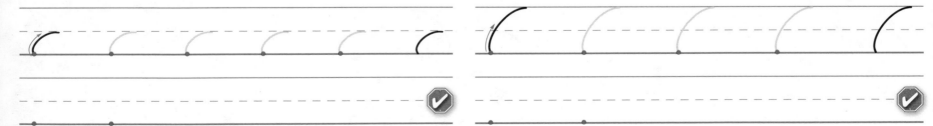

Slant

A **slant** is one of the basic strokes used to write cursive letters.

A slant stroke slides down.

Trace a slant stroke in each lowercase letter.

a   b   d   f   g   h   i

j   k   l   m   t   u   y

Trace a slant stroke in each uppercase letter.

A   B   K   P   R   U   X   Y

Trace and write slant strokes.

Keys to Legibility

Size

Shape

To make your lowercase cursive letters easy to read, pay attention to the four Keys to Legibility.

Shape Look at the shape of each letter.

There are four basic strokes in cursive writing.

undercurve	downcurve	overcurve	slant

Circle each letter that has an undercurve beginning.

i   t   a

Circle each letter that has a downcurve beginning. ⌐

w   d   g

Circle each letter that has an overcurve beginning. ⌐

b   m   n

Circle each letter that has a slant stroke. ╱

o   k   g

60

Size Look at the size of each letter.

Tall Letters
Tall letters touch the headline.

b d k

Short Letters
Short letters touch the midline.

a c e

Letters With Descenders
Some letters have descenders that go below the baseline.

g j f

Circle the tall letters.

a c d e h i l t

Circle the short letters.

l m k o e b t v

Circle the letters that have descenders.

p q r t f j x z

Keys to Legibility

Slant
Spacing

To make your lowercase cursive letters easy to read, pay attention to the four Keys to Legibility.

Spacing  Look at the spacing between letters and words. There should be space for ◯ between letters.

aanbs

Circle the word that has good letter spacing.

ants   *ants*   *ants*

There should be space for \ between words.

little ants

Circle the phrase that has good word spacing.

some   *little*   *ants*

some little ants

some little ants

Slant

Look at the slant of your letters.

Cursive letters have a forward slant.

forward slant

POSITION
PULL
SHIFT

To write with good slant:

- Check your paper **position**.
- **Pull** your downstrokes in the proper direction.
- **Shift** your paper as you write.

If you are left-handed . . .

pull toward your left elbow.

If you are right-handed . . .

pull toward the middle of your body.

Circle the word that has good slant.

butterfly　　　*butterfly*

People

Some people talk and talk
and never say a thing.
Some people look at you
and birds begin to sing.

Some people laugh and laugh
and yet you want to cry.
Some people touch your hand
and music fills the sky.

Charlotte Zolotow

Writing Lowercase Cursive Letters

Get ready,
Get set,
Go cursive!

Let's begin with lowercase letters.
As you learn to write in cursive, you'll learn
to read it, too. You will learn to write each letter.
Then you'll join letters and write words.

Undercurve Letters

You will learn to write these lowercase letters. Each letter begins with an undercurve stroke.

i   *t*   *u*   *w*   *e*   *l*   *b*

h   *f*   *k*   *r*   *s*   *j*   *p*

Trace and write undercurve strokes.

Downcurve Letters

You will learn to write these lowercase letters. Each letter begins with a downcurve stroke.

a *d* *g* *o* *c* *q*

Trace and write downcurve strokes.

Overcurve Letters

You will learn to write these lowercase letters. Each letter begins with an overcurve stroke.

n *m* *y* *x* *v* *z*

Trace and write overcurve strokes.

Circle i and *i* in these words.

interesting insects

interesting insects

Trace and write. Notice the undercurve beginning.

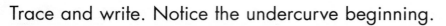

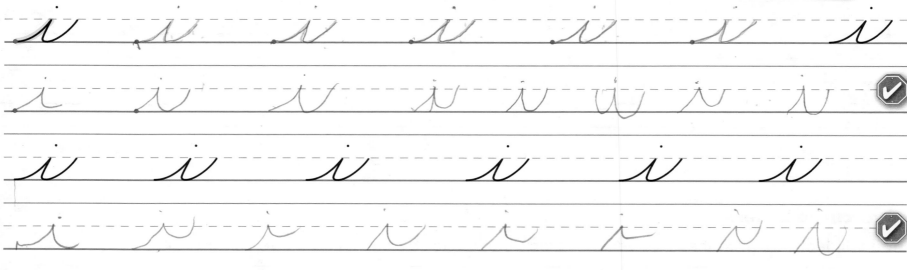

Join *i* and *i*. The ending stroke of the first letter begins the second letter.

Stroke description to guide letter formation at home:
1. Undercurve.
2. Slant; undercurve. Lift.
3. Dot.

Stop and Check
Circle your best *i*.

Circle t and *t* in these words.

tractor tilling

tractor tilling

Trace and write. Notice the undercurve ending.

Join *t* and other letters.

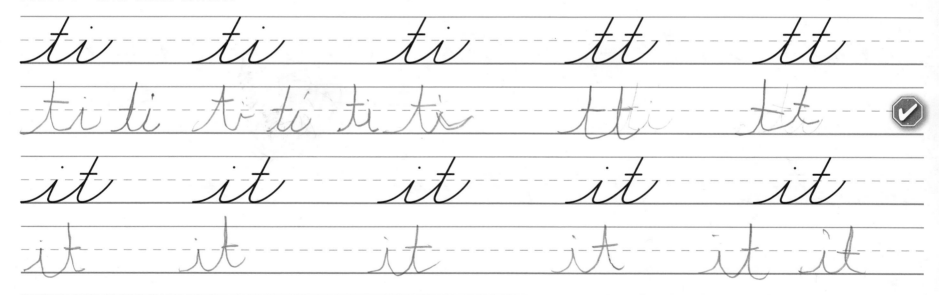

School Home

Stroke description to guide letter formation at home:
1. Undercurve.
2. Slant; undercurve. Lift.
3. Slide right.

Size
Circle your best tall letter.

69

Circle u and *u* in these words.

useful umbrella

useful umbrella

Trace and write. Notice the undercurve beginning.

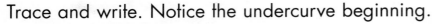

u   u   u   u   u   u   u

u   u   u   u   u   u   u ✔

Join *u* and other letters.

ui   ut   uit   iu   tu

✔

tutu   tutu   tutu

Stroke description to guide letter formation at home:
u
1. Undercurve.
2. Slant; undercurve.
3. Slant; undercurve.

Stop and Check
Circle your best *u*.

Circle w and _w_ in these words.

winter wind blows

winter wind blows

Trace and write. Notice the checkstroke (‿) ending.

_w   w   w   w   w   w   w_

_w   w   w   w   w   w_ ✓

Join _w_ and other letters.

wi   wt   tw   twi

wi   twi   wi   wi ✓

wit   wit   wit   wit

wit   wit

School Home

Stroke description to guide letter formation at home:
1. Undercurve.
2. Slant; undercurve.
3. Slant; undercurve.
4. Checkstroke.

Spacing
Circle your best joining.

71

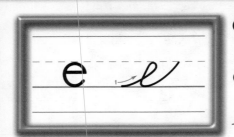

Circle e and *e* in these words.

elephant ears

elephant ears

Trace and write.

e   e   e   e   e   e   e

Join *e* and other letters.

ei   et   ew   ie   te

ewe   wet   tweet   tie

Stroke description to guide letter formation at home:

1. Undercurve; loop back; slant; undercurve.

e

School Home

72

Stop and Check

Circle your best *e*.

Circle l and *l* in these words.

l *l*

lions lying

lions lying

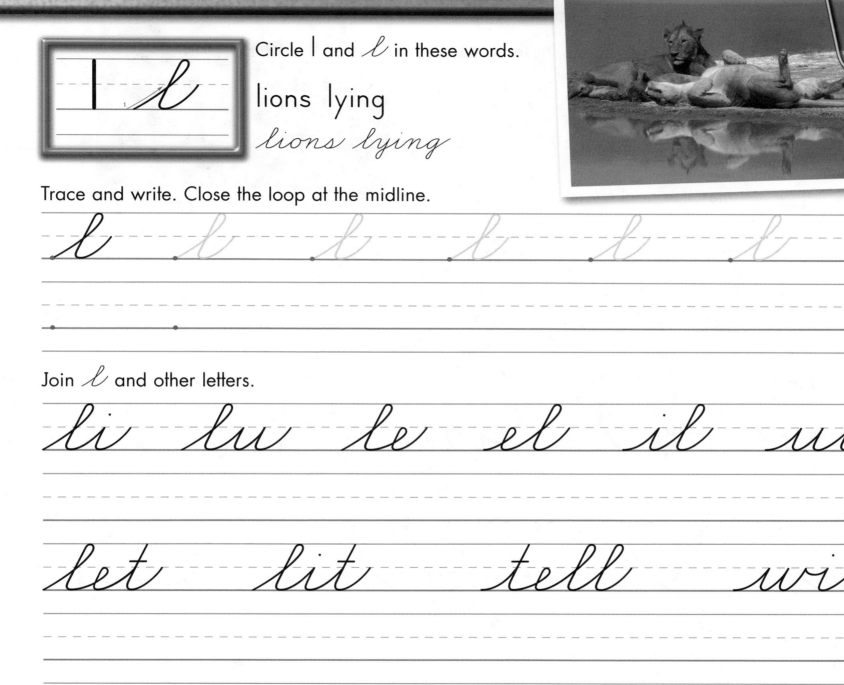

Trace and write. Close the loop at the midline.

l   l   l   l   l   l   l ✓

Join *l* and other letters.

li   lu   le   el   il   ul ✓

let   lit   tell   will

Stroke description to guide letter formation at home:

l   l. Undercurve; loop back;
      slant; undercurve.

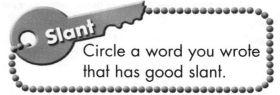
Slant

Circle a word you wrote
that has good slant.

73

Circle b and *b* in these words.

blue bike

blue bike

Trace and write. Notice the checkstroke (⌣) ending.

b   b   b   b   b   b   b

✓

Join *b* and other letters.

bl   be   bi   bu   ib   eb

✓

but   bite   built   blue

School Home

Stroke description to guide letter formation at home:

b
1. Undercurve; loop back; slant; undercurve.
2. Checkstroke.

74

Stop and Check
Circle your best *b*.

Write the joinings and the words.

Undercurve-to-Undercurve Joining
The undercurve ending continues up toward the midline or the headline
to form the undercurve of the next letter.

ue   *ib*   *ill*   *lute*

Checkstroke-to-Undercurve Joining
The checkstroke ending ⌣ swings right to form the undercurve beginning
of the next letter.

wu   *be*   *web*   *belt*

Stop and Check
Circle your best joining.

75

Review

i t u w e l b

Write the letter joinings.

ti   tu   tw   el   ub

wi   li   bu   eb   ut

Write the words.

it   well   tube   bell

76

Use the letters in the box to make as many words as you can.
Write the words in your best cursive handwriting.

i   t   u   w   e   l   b

tub

Stop and Check

Circle your best letter.

In the Real World

The more you practice writing in cursive, the easier it will be!

In class, you wrote a short story. After you finished your draft, you highlighted five words that you had spelled incorrectly. On the guidelines below, write the misspelled words correctly, in cursive. Writing the words again will help you remember them.

One day, Beth blue such a big soap bubble that she floated up into the big blew sky. Everything looked very littel from so high up. Soon, it started to rain. Beth was getting whet, so she popped the bubble and ran to tel her friends about her adventure.

Circle h and *h* in these words.

horses have hay

horses have hay

Trace and write.

h h h h h h h h ✔

Join *h* and other letters.

hu hi he th wh ✔

hill the white wheel

School Home

Stroke description to guide letter formation at home:

h
1. Undercurve; loop back; slant.
2. Overcurve; slant; undercurve.

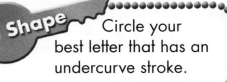

Shape

Circle your best letter that has an undercurve stroke.

Circle f and *f* in these words.

field of flowers

field of flowers

Trace and write. Close the bottom loop at the baseline.

f   f   f   f   f   f ✓

Join *f* and other letters.

fi   fe   ft   fl   if   ife ✓

feel   fill   life   left

Stroke description to guide letter formation at home:

1. Undercurve; loop back; slant; loop forward.
2. Undercurve.

Stop and Check

Circle your best *f*.

Circle k and *k* in these words.

kittens drink milk

kittens drink milk

Trace and write.

k *k* *k* *k* *k* *k* *k*

Join *k* and other letters.

ke *ki* *kl* *ilk* *ike*

kite *like* *hike* *elk*

Stroke description to guide letter formation at home:

1. Undercurve; loop back; slant.
2. Overcurve; curve forward; curve under.
3. Slant right; undercurve.

Size

Circle your best tall letter.

r ℛ

Circle r and ℛ in these words.

riding at a ranch

riding at a ranch

Trace and write.

ℛ ℛ ℛ ℛ ℛ ℛ ℛ

Join ℛ and other letters.

ri re er te fr br

rub here writer free

Stroke description to guide letter formation at home:

1. Undercurve.
2. Slant right.
3. Slant; undercurve.

Stop and Check

Circle your best ℛ.

s s

Circle s and s in these words.

seals swimming

seals swimming

Trace and write.

s   s   s   s   s   s   ✔

Join s and other letters.

si   se   sl   st   sw   sk   ✔

see   sister   still   self

school Home

Stroke description to guide letter formation at home:
1. Undercurve.
2. Curve down and back.
3. Undercurve.

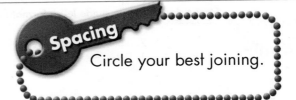
Spacing
Circle your best joining.

83

Circle j and *j* in these words.

jolly juggler
jolly juggler

Trace and write. Notice the overcurve ending.

j   j   j   j   j   j   j

Join *j* and other letters.

je   ju   jui   ji   ej

just   jest   jewel   jet

Stroke description to guide letter formation at home:
1. Undercurve.
2. Slant; loop back; overcurve. Lift.
3. Dot.

School Home

84

Stop and Check
Circle your best *j*.

Circle p and *p* in these words.

pile of pencils

pile of pencils

Trace and write.

p   p   p   p   p   p   p

Join *p* and other letters.

pe   pi   pl   ph   sp   lp

purr   put   pull   help

Stroke description to guide letter formation at home:

1. Undercurve.
2. Slant; loop back; overcurve; curve back.
3. Undercurve.

Slant
Circle a word you wrote
that has good slant.

85

h f k r s j p

Write the words.

keep   rush   just

first   trip   full

Write the phrase.

three little sheep

Read the words in the box. On the lines below, write the words in alphabetical order. Use your best cursive handwriting.

push whisper turtle help surprise
bush rest life fish useful

1. _____

2. _____

3. _____

4. _____

5. _____

6. _____

7. _____

8. _____

9. _____

10. _____

Stop and Check
Circle your best word.

87

Circle a and a in these words.

army of ants

army of ants

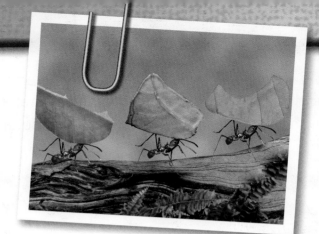

Trace and write. Notice the downcurve beginning.

a a a a a a a ✓

Join a and other letters.

as al ba wa ha ✓

are artist ball batter

school Home

Stroke description to guide letter formation at home:
1. Downcurve; undercurve.
2. Slant; undercurve.

a

88

Stop and Check
Circle your best *a*.

Circle d and d in these words.

desert dune

desert dune

Trace and write. Notice the downcurve beginning.

d d d d d d d

Join d and other letters.

de   *da*   *ad*   *id*   *ld*   *rd*

did   *dad*   *desk*   *wide*

School Home

Stroke description to guide letter formation at home:
1. Downcurve; undercurve.
2. Slant; undercurve.

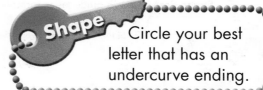
Shape   Circle your best letter that has an undercurve ending.

89

Circle g and *g* in these words.

growing grapes

growing grapes

Trace and write. Notice the overcurve ending.

g   g   g   g   g   g   g

Join *g* and other letters.

gi   gu   ga   ge   gr   ag

get   giraffe   guess   flag

Stroke description to guide letter formation at home:
1. Downcurve; undercurve.
2. Slant; loop back; overcurve.

Stop and Check
Circle your best *g*.

Circle o and *o* in these words.

owls hoot

owls hoot

Trace and write. Notice the checkstroke (⌣) ending.

o   o   o   o   o   o   o

Join *o* and other letters.

ot   od   ow   bo   lo   jo

of   off   old   orbit   oh

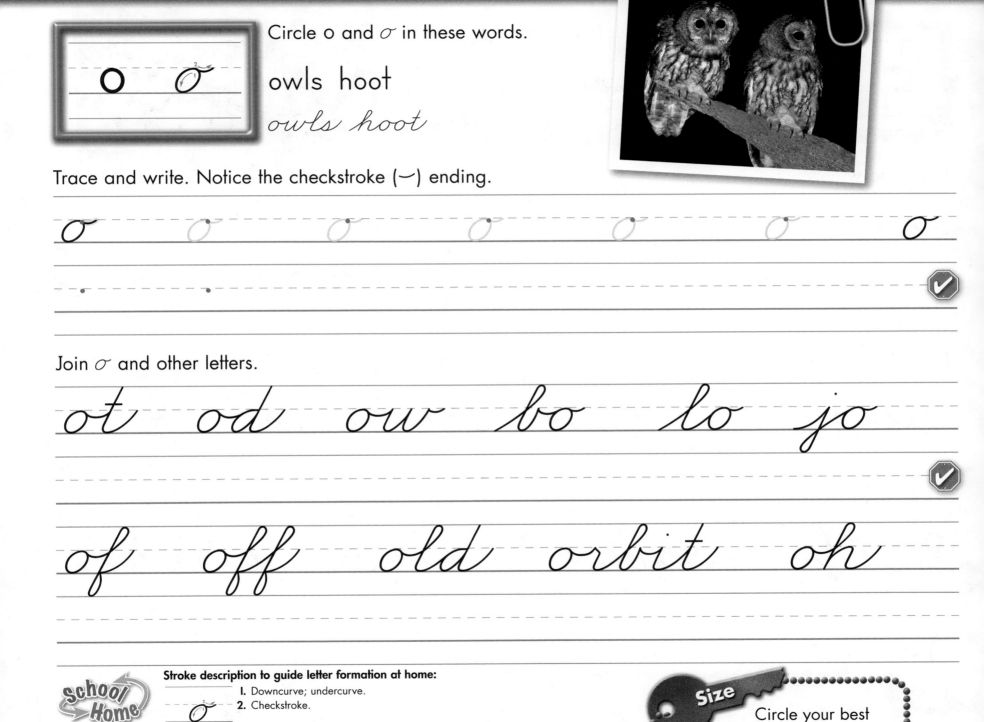
School Home

Stroke description to guide letter formation at home:
1. Downcurve; undercurve.
2. Checkstroke.

Size

Circle your best
short letter.

91

Circle c and $\mathcal{C}$ in these words.

cowboy corrals cows

cowboy corrals cows

Trace and write.

$\mathcal{C}$ $\mathcal{C}$ $\mathcal{C}$ $\mathcal{C}$ $\mathcal{C}$ $\mathcal{C}$ $\mathcal{C}$

Join $\mathcal{C}$ and other letters.

ca co ce ci ch ck

call color cat chick

Stroke description to guide letter formation at home:

1. Downcurve; undercurve.

c

92

Stop and Check

Circle your best $\mathcal{C}$.

Circle q and *q* in these words.

ducks quack

ducks quack

Trace and write.

q   *q*   *q*   *q*   *q*   *q*   q

Join *q* and other letters.

qu   qui   qua   quo   que

quit   quilt   quiet   quail

Stroke description to guide letter formation at home:

q
1. Downcurve; undercurve.
2. Slant; loop forward.
3. Undercurve.

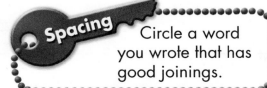

Spacing

Circle a word you wrote that has good joinings.

a d g o c q

Write the words.

quick   *add*   *cage*

code   *odd*   *goat*

Write the phrase.

a good job

Each sentence below is missing a word. Choose a word from the word box that best completes each sentence. Write the words in cursive on the guidelines.

> *before   quiet   because   through   should*

What ___ I wear to school today?

I brush my teeth ___ I go to school.

I walk ___ town to get to school.

I must be ___ while my teacher is talking.

I like school ___ it is fun!

- Shape — Circle your best letter that has a downcurve beginning.
- Size — Circle your best short letter.
- Spacing — Circle a word you wrote that has good spacing.
- Slant — Circle a word you wrote that has good slant.

Circle n and *n* in these words.

n *n*

bunnies nibbling
bunnies nibbling

Trace and write. Notice the overcurve beginning.

n   n   n   n   n   n   n

Join *n* and other letters.

ni   ne   na   in   an

new not nine bunnies

School Home

Stroke description to guide letter formation at home:
1. Overcurve; slant.
n 2. Overcurve; slant; undercurve.

96

Stop and Check
Circle your best *n*.

Circle m and *m* in these words.

muddy mischief

muddy mischief

Trace and write.

m m m m m m m

Join *m* and other letters.

mi ma mo om am

mean men moon comb

School Home

Stroke description to guide letter formation at home:
1. Overcurve; slant.
2. Overcurve; slant.
3. Overcurve; slant; undercurve.

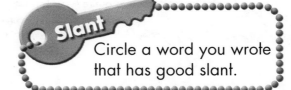
Slant
Circle a word you wrote that has good slant.

97

Circle y and *y* in these words.

young yak

young yak

Trace and write.

y   y   y   y   y   y   y ✓

Join *y* and other letters.

yo   yu   ye   ty   cy   gy ✓

yard   yams   yours   try

Stroke description to guide letter formation at home:
1. Overcurve; slant; undercurve.
2. Slant; loop back; overcurve.

y

Stop and Check

Circle your best *y* .

Circle x and x in these words.

Alex's experiment

Trace and write.

x x x x x x x ✓

Join x and other letters.

xy xc ix ex ox ax ✓

mix $xylophone$ $exercise$

Stroke description to guide letter formation at home:
1. Overcurve; slant; undercurve. Lift.
2. Slant.

Shape
Circle your best
short letter.

99

V $\mathcal{V}$

Circle v and $\mathcal{v}$ in these words.

village in a valley

village in a valley

Trace and write.

$\mathcal{V}$ $\mathcal{V}$ $\mathcal{V}$ $\mathcal{V}$ $\mathcal{V}$ $\mathcal{V}$ $\mathcal{V}$

Join $\mathcal{v}$ and other letters.

va   *vi*   *ove*   *ive*   *ave*

vine   *voice*   *love*   *give*

School Home

Stroke description to guide letter formation at home:

1. Overcurve; slant; undercurve.
$\mathcal{V}$ 2. Checkstroke.

Stop and Check

Circle your best $\mathcal{V}$.

Circle z and *z* in these words.

z *Z*

zesty pizza
zesty pizza

Trace and write.

z   z   z   z   z   z   z

Join *z* and other letters.

ze   zy   oze   ize   eze

zoo   zipper   size   fuzzy

Stroke description to guide letter formation at home:
1. Overcurve; slant.
2. Overcurve; curve down; loop; overcurve.

Size

Circle your best letter that has a descender.

Review

n m y x v z

Write the words.

zoom myself next zoo

mix giving never

Write the phrase.

six shiny new vans

102

Draw a line to match each animal with the color that describes it best. Then write the two words together to form a phrase on each line below.

canary	green
polar bear	brown
beaver	yellow
flamingo	white
lizard	pink

yellow canary

Shape — Circle your best letter that has an overcurve beginning.

Size — Circle your best short letter.

Spacing — Circle a word you wrote that has good spacing.

Slant — Circle a word you wrote that has good slant.

Keys to Legibility

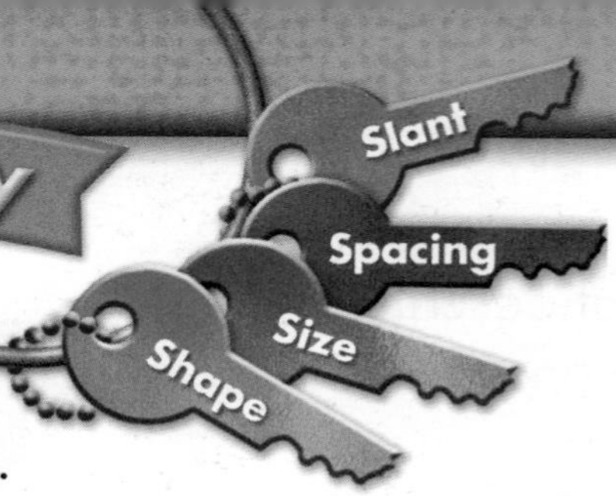
Slant
Spacing
Size
Shape

Write the poem.
Make your writing easy to read.

winter snow sparkles

tiny snowflakes fall

each one is different

catch one on my tongue

smile big and bright

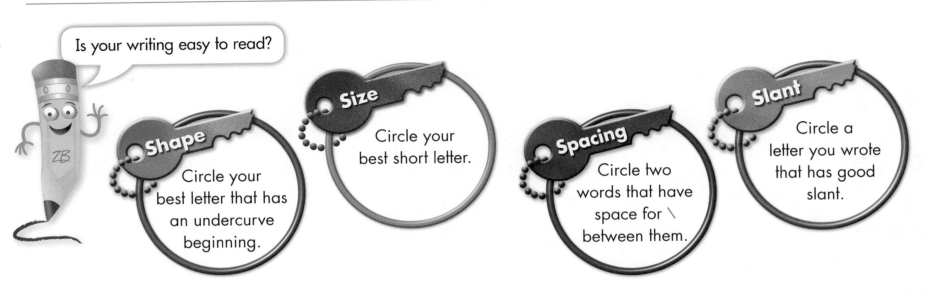

Is your writing easy to read?

Shape
Circle your best letter that has an undercurve beginning.

Size
Circle your best short letter.

Spacing
Circle two words that have space for \ between them.

Slant
Circle a letter you wrote that has good slant.

Lowercase Cursive Review

Write these lowercase letters in cursive.

i t u w

e l b h f k

r s j p

a d g o c q

n m y x v z

Write these words in cursive.

does

have

quick

once

Write these phrases in your best cursive handwriting.

a creepy crawly spider

busy buzzing bees

clever sly foxes

a great big bear

My writing has good **Shape** · □
My writing has good **Size** · □
My writing has good **Spacing** · □
My writing has good **Slant** · □

107

Cursive Numerals and Number Words

Trace and write.

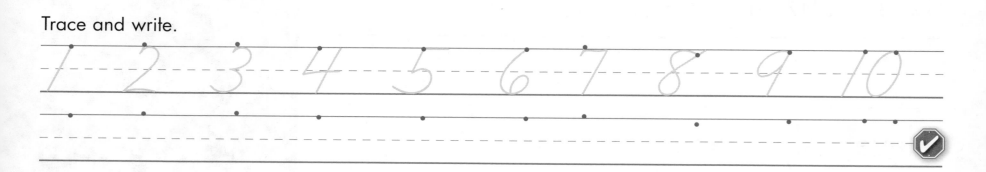

Fill in the missing numerals on the doors.

Write the number words.

one   two   three   four

five   six   seven

eight   nine   ten

Write the answers to the number sentences in words.

1 + 3 = _____

7 + 2 = _____

8 - 3 = _____

My writing has good Shape . ☐
My writing has good Size . ☐
My writing has good Spacing . ☐
My writing has good Slant . ☐

Writing Uppercase Cursive Letters

Downcurve Letters

You will learn to write these uppercase letters. Each letter has a downcurve stroke.

a *O* *D* *C* *E*

Trace and write downcurve strokes.

Curve Forward Letters

You will learn to write these uppercase letters. Each letter begins with a curve forward stroke.

N *M* *H* *K* *U*

Y *Z* *V* *W* *X*

Trace and write curve forward-slant strokes.

Overcurve Letters

You will learn to write these uppercase letters that begin with an overcurve stroke.

Trace and write overcurve strokes.

Undercurve-Loop Letters

You will learn to write these uppercase letters that begin with an undercurve and a loop stroke.

Trace and write undercurve-loop strokes.

Doublecurve Letters

You will learn to write these uppercase letters that have doublecurve strokes.

Trace and write doublecurve strokes.

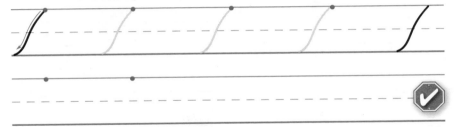

Undercurve-Slant Letters

You will learn to write these uppercase letters that begin with an undercurve and a slant stroke.

Trace and write undercurve-slant strokes.

 **A** *a*

Circle A and *a* in these words.

Amanda likes art class.

Amanda likes art class.

Trace and write.

a   a   a   a   a   a   a

a is joined to the letter that follows. Write the words that begin with *a*. Write the sentence.

Adam   Anna   August

Art class is a favorite.

Stroke description to guide letter formation at home:

a
  1. Downcurve; undercurve.
  2. Slant; undercurve.

Stop and Check
Circle your best *a*.

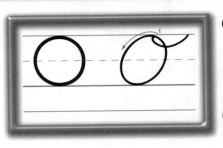

Circle O and O in these words.

Oysters live in the ocean.

Oysters live in the ocean.

Trace and write.

O is not joined to the letter that follows. Write the words that begin with O. Write the sentence.

October   Oscar   Olivia

Octopuses live there, too.

School Home

Stroke description to guide letter formation at home:
I. Downcurve; undercurve; loop; curve right.

Spacing
Circle your best joining.

Circle D and $\mathcal{D}$ in these words.

Do the dishes.

Do the dishes.

Trace and write.

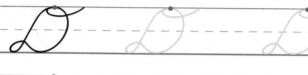

$\mathcal{D}$ is not joined to the letter that follows. Write the words that begin with $\mathcal{D}$. Write the sentence.

Dani Devon December

Don't drop the dishes!

Stroke description to guide letter formation at home:

1. Downcurve; loop; curve down and up; loop; curve right.

Stop and Check

Circle your best $\mathcal{D}$.

Circle C and _C_ in these words.

Cats chase mice.

Cats chase mice.

Trace and write.

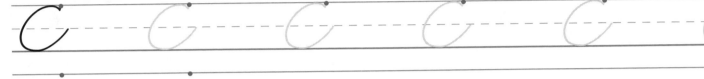

_C_ is joined to the letter that follows. Write the words that begin with _C_. Write the sentence.

Colin   California   Cara

Cats can run fast.

Stroke description to guide letter formation at home:

1. Slant.
2. Downcurve; undercurve.

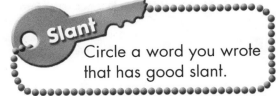
Slant

Circle a word you wrote that has good slant.

115

Circle E and $\mathcal{E}$ in these words.

Eagles lay eggs.

Eagles lay eggs.

Trace and write.

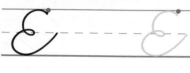

$\mathcal{E}$ is joined to the letter that follows. Write the words that begin with $\mathcal{E}$. Write the sentence.

Evan   Ellie   Erica

Eagles feed their babies.

Stroke description to guide letter formation at home:

1. Slant.
2. Downcurve; loop; downcurve; undercurve.

Stop and Check

Circle your best $\mathcal{E}$.

The cursive letters $\mathcal{O}$ and $\mathcal{D}$ are not joined to the letter that follows.

Joining a, c, and e

The letters a, c, and e are joined to the letter that follows. Write the names below, paying close attention to the joinings. Each joining must be wide enough to allow room for joining the next letter.

Alexis   *Aiden*   *Abby*

Connor   *Chloe*   *Carlos*

Ethan   *Emily*   *Evan*

Stop and Check

Circle your best joining.

117

a   O   D   C   E

Write the names of cities.

Chicago   Atlanta

Detroit   Omaha

Write the sentence.

Eve is going to Dallas.

Write a complete sentence using a name and a city from the columns below. The first sentence is written as an example.

Dan   Orlando

Anna   Erie

Ella   Columbus

Cara   Austin

Omar   Denver

Dan went to Orlando.

Circle your best letter that has a downcurve beginning.

Circle your best tall letter.

Circle two words that have space for \ between them.

Circle a word you wrote that has good slant.

Cursive Writing

In the Real World

Learning to write neatly in cursive will make your handwriting easier for others to read. This can be useful when writing an invitation.

Write the invitation using your best cursive handwriting. Remember to leave space for margins.

Come One, Come All!
At: Elizabeth Diaz's house
Address: 183 Elderbury Drive
Date: April 30
Come help us celebrate!

Circle N and *n* in these words.

Nate and Nick look alike.

Nate and Nick look alike.

Trace and write.

n   n   n   n   n   n   n

n is joined to the letter that follows. Write the words that begin with *n*. Write the sentence.

Nashville November Nell

Nate and Nick are twins.

Stroke description to guide letter formation at home:
1. Curve forward; slant.
2. Overcurve; slant; undercurve.

School Home

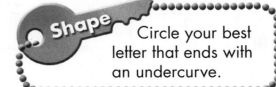

Shape
Circle your best letter that ends with an undercurve.

121

Circle M and $\mathcal{M}$ in these words.

Moose live in Maine.

Moose live in Maine.

Trace and write.

$\mathcal{m}$ $\mathcal{m}$ $\mathcal{m}$ $\mathcal{m}$ $\mathcal{m}$ $\mathcal{m}$ $\mathcal{m}$

$\mathcal{m}$ is joined to the letter that follows. Write the words that begin with $\mathcal{m}$. Write the sentence.

Monday   May   March

Mike saw a moose.

School Home

Stroke description to guide letter formation at home:

1. Curve forward; slant.
2. Overcurve; slant.
3. Overcurve; slant; undercurve.

Stop and Check

Circle your best $\mathcal{m}$.

122

Circle H and $\mathcal{H}$ in these words.

Hallie's birthday is today.

Hallie's birthday is today.

Trace and write.

$\mathcal{H}$ $\mathcal{H}$ $\mathcal{H}$ $\mathcal{H}$ $\mathcal{H}$ $\mathcal{H}$ $\mathcal{H}$

$\mathcal{H}$ is joined to the letter that follows. Write the words that begin with $\mathcal{H}$. Write the sentence.

Hudson Hawaii Hannah

Happy birthday, Hallie!

Stroke description to guide letter formation at home:

1. Curve forward; slant. Lift.
2. Curve back; slant.
3. Retrace; loop; curve right.

School Home

Size

Circle your best tall letter.

Circle K and $\mathcal{K}$ in these words.

Kyle is kind.

Kyle is kind.

Trace and write.

$\mathcal{K}$ $\mathcal{K}$ $\mathcal{K}$ $\mathcal{K}$ $\mathcal{K}$ $\mathcal{K}$ $\mathcal{K}$

$\mathcal{K}$ is joined to the letter that follows. Write the words that begin with $\mathcal{K}$. Write the sentence.

Kentucky Kendra Kai

Kyle likes to share.

Stroke description to guide letter formation at home:

$\mathcal{K}$

1. Curve forward; slant. Lift.
2. Doublecurve.
3. Curve forward and down; undercurve.

Stop and Check
Circle your best $\mathcal{K}$.

Circle U and $\mathcal{U}$ in these words.

Underwater diving is fun.

Underwater diving is fun.

Trace and write.

$\mathcal{U}$ $\mathcal{U}$ $\mathcal{U}$ $\mathcal{U}$ $\mathcal{U}$ $\mathcal{U}$ $\mathcal{U}$

$\mathcal{U}$ is joined to the letter that follows. Write the words that begin with $\mathcal{U}$. Write the sentence.

Utah   United Kingdom

Using goggles is smart.

Stroke description to guide letter formation at home:
$\mathcal{U}$
1. Curve forward; slant; undercurve.
2. Slant; undercurve.

Spacing
Circle your best joining.

125

Write the names of books.

Under My Nose   *Heidi*

Monkey King   *Madeline*

Write the sentence.

Kylie read a good book.

My writing has good  Shape ☐

My writing has good Size ☐

126

Read the names of authors below. Write them in cursive on the lines in alphabetical order according to their last name.

Mercer Mayer   *Kaye Umansky*   *Holly Black*

Kevin Henkes   *Nancy Carlson*

Shape   Circle your best letter that begins with a curve forward-slant stroke.

Size   Circle your best tall letter.

Spacing   Circle a word you wrote that has good spacing.

Slant   Circle a word you wrote that has good slant.

Circle Y and *Y* in these words.

Yuri likes yellow.

Yuri likes yellow.

Trace and write.

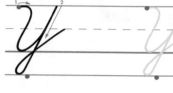 *Y Y Y Y Y Y Y*

Y is joined to the letter that follows. Write words that begin with *Y*. Write the sentence.

Yan   Yaelle   Yumi

Yuri has a yellow bike.

Stroke description to guide letter formation at home:

1. Curve forward; slant; undercurve.
2. Slant; loop back; overcurve.

School Home

128

Stop and Check
Circle your best *Y*.

Circle Z and *Z* in these words.

Zoey likes pizza.

Zoey likes pizza.

Trace and write.

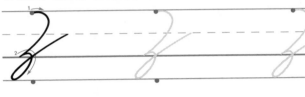

Z is joined to the letter that follows. Write words that begin with *Z*. Write the sentence.

Zambia   Zog   Ze Ze

Zoey uses a fork.

Stroke description to guide letter formation at home:
1. Curve forward and down; slant.
2. Overcurve; curve down; loop; overcurve.

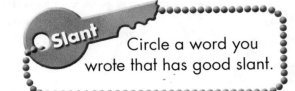
Slant
Circle a word you
wrote that has good slant.

129

Circle V and $\mathcal{V}$ in these words.

Val buys vegetables.

Val buys vegetables.

Trace and write.

$\mathcal{V}$ ⟍ $\mathcal{V}$ ⟍ $\mathcal{V}$ ⟍ $\mathcal{V}$ ⟍ $\mathcal{V}$ ⟍ $\mathcal{V}$

$\mathcal{V}$ is not joined to the letter that follows. Write words that begin with $\mathcal{V}$. Write the sentence.

Venezuela   Vernon

Val's mother cooks soup.

Stroke description to guide letter formation at home:

$\mathcal{V}$ 1. Curve forward; slant; undercurve; overcurve.

130

Stop and Check

Circle your best $\mathcal{V}$.

W W

Circle W and W in these words.

Wes walks his dogs.

Wes walks his dogs.

Trace and write.

W W W W W W W W

W is not joined to the letter that follows. Write words that begin with W. Write the sentence.

Washington Wednesday

Wes will be tired.

School Home

Stroke description to guide letter formation at home:
1. Curve forward; slant; undercurve.
2. Slant; undercurve; overcurve.

Shape
Circle your best letter that has a curve forward-slant stroke.

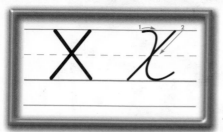

Circle X and $\mathcal{X}$ in these words.

Xander had an X-ray.

Xander had an X-ray.

Trace and write.

$\mathcal{X}$ $\mathcal{X}$ $\mathcal{X}$ $\mathcal{X}$ $\mathcal{X}$ $\mathcal{X}$ $\mathcal{X}$ ✓

$\mathcal{X}$ is not joined to the letter that follows. Write words that begin with $\mathcal{X}$. Write the sentence.

Xian   *Xavier*   *Xota*

X-ray machines are big.

School Home

Stroke description to guide letter formation at home:

$\mathcal{X}$ 1. Curve forward; slant; undercurve. Lift.
   2. Slant.

132

Stop and Check
Circle your best $\mathcal{X}$.

Joining *y* and *z*

The letters *y* and *z* are joined to the letter that follows.
In the overcurve-to-undercurve joining, the overcurve ending in *y* and *z*
changes direction at the baseline to form the undercurve beginning of the
next letter. Write the joinings.

Ye   Yi   Yu   Ze   Zi   Zu

In the overcurve-to-downcurve joining, the overcurve ending in *y* and *z*
crosses at the baseline and then continues up and wide to form the downcurve beginning of the next letter. Write the joinings.

Ya   Yo   Za   Zo

> The cursive letters *V*, *W*, and *X* are
> not joined to the letter that follows.

Stop and Check

Circle your best joining.

133

Y Z V W X

Write the names of places.

Washington   Yosemite

Xenia   Mount Vernon

Write the sentence.

We are at the Dallas Zoo.

Read the names of animals in the box below. Choose the animal that best fits each description. Then write a sentence that best tells what each person saw.

lions   zebras   giraffes   elephants   penguins

Zak saw black and white animals that swim and eat fish.

Zak saw penguins.

Victoria saw yellow animals with brown spots and long necks.

Will saw black and white striped animals with four legs.

Xiang saw large gray animals with big ears and long trunks.

Shape — Circle your best letter that begins with a curve forward-slant stroke.

Size — Circle your best tall letter.

Spacing — Circle two letters that have space for ○ between them.

Slant — Circle a word you wrote that has good slant.

In the Real World

Using cursive will help you write more quickly. This will be useful when taking notes in class. Write the notes about Amelia Earhart. Remember to leave space for margins.

1897: Was born in Kansas

1932: Was first woman to fly solo across Atlantic Ocean

1937: Amelia began flight around world, but plane was lost

Stop and Check
Circle your best uppercase letter.

Circle I and $\mathscr{I}$ in these words.

Is Inez a fast runner?

Is Inez a fast runner?

Trace and write.

$\mathscr{I}$ is not joined to the letter that follows. Write words that begin with $\mathscr{I}$. Write the sentence.

Ike   Ida   Illinois

I think Inez ran fast.

School Home

Stroke description to guide letter formation at home:

1. Overcurve; curve down and up.
2. Retrace; curve right.

Size

Circle your best
tall letter.

J J

Circle J and *J* in these words.

Jena jumps rope in June.

Jena jumps rope in June.

Trace and write.

J J J J J J J J

J is joined to the letter that follows. Write words that begin with *J*. Write the sentence.

January   José   Jacques

Jena rests in July.

Stroke description to guide letter formation at home:

1. Overcurve; slant; loop back; overcurve.

Stop and Check
Circle your best *J*.

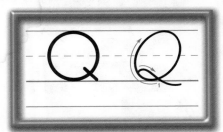

Circle Q and Q in these words.

Quila stands in line.

Quila stands in line.

Trace and write.

 Q ____ Q ____ Q ____ Q ____ Q ____ Q ____ Q

Q is not joined to the letter that follows. Write words that begin with Q. Write the sentence.

Quincy   Quejo   Quinn

Quila waits her turn.

Stroke description to guide letter formation at home:

1. Curve back; overcurve; curve down; retrace; curve forward; curve under.

 Spacing
Circle a word you wrote that has good joinings.

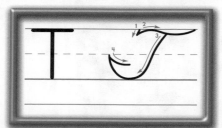

Circle T and $\mathcal{T}$ in these words.

The class took a trip.

The class took a trip.

Trace and write.

$\mathcal{T}$ $\mathcal{T}$ $\mathcal{T}$ $\mathcal{T}$ $\mathcal{T}$ $\mathcal{T}$ $\mathcal{T}$

$\mathcal{T}$ is not joined to the letter that follows. Write words that begin with $\mathcal{T}$. Write the sentence.

Thursday   *Tuesday*

Their teacher went, too.

Stroke description to guide letter formation at home:

1. Slant.
2. Curve forward and right. Lift.
3. Doublecurve; curve up.
4. Retrace; curve right.

140

Stop and Check
Circle your best $\mathcal{T}$.

Circle F and $\mathcal{F}$ in these words.

Fall leaves fall on Finn.

Fall leaves fall on Finn.

Trace and write.

 $\mathcal{F}$ $\mathcal{F}$ $\mathcal{F}$ $\mathcal{F}$ $\mathcal{F}$ $\mathcal{F}$ $\mathcal{F}$ $\mathcal{F}$

$\mathcal{F}$ is not joined to the letter that follows. Write words that begin with $\mathcal{F}$. Write the sentence.

February   Friday

Finn loves fall colors.

Stroke description to guide letter formation at home:

1. Slant.
2. Curve forward and right. Lift.
3. Doublecurve; curve up.
4. Retrace; curve right. Lift.
5. Slide right.

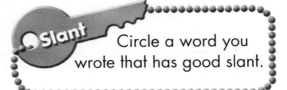
Slant — Circle a word you wrote that has good slant.

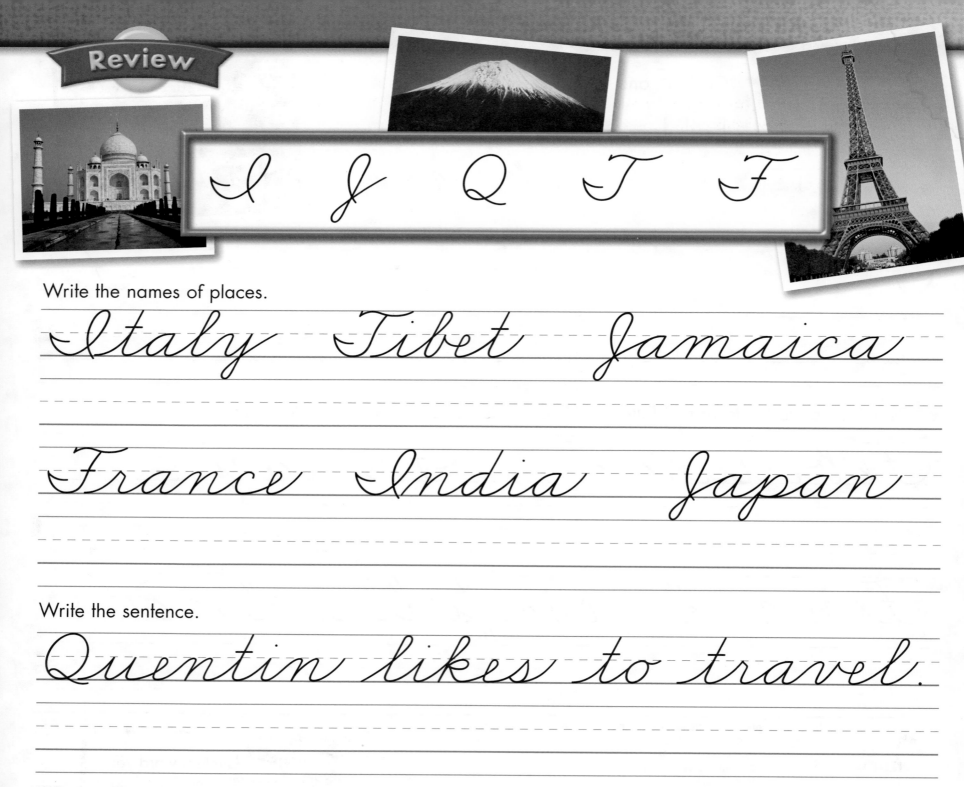

Review

I J Q T F

Write the names of places.

Italy   Tibet   Jamaica

France   India   Japan

Write the sentence.

Quentin likes to travel.

Application

Listed below are some famous places Quinn visited and what he saw there.
Write a sentence about the countries Quinn visited.

Turkey: Topkapi Palace   India: Taj Mahal   Japan: Mount Fuji   France: Eiffel Tower

Quinn visited Topkapi Palace.

Quinn went to Turkey.

Quinn visited the Eiffel Tower.

Quinn visited the Taj Mahal.

Quinn visited Mount Fuji.

Shape Circle your best letter that has an overcurve stroke.
Size Circle your best tall letter.
Spacing Circle a word you wrote that has good spacing.
Slant Circle a word you wrote that has good slant.

143

Circle G and *G* in these words.

Gordy has a question.

Gordy has a question.

Trace and write.

G is not joined to the letter that follows. Write words that begin with *G*. Write the sentence.

Gloria   *Greg*   *Grace*

Gina knows the answer.

Stroke description to guide letter formation at home:

1. Undercurve; loop; curve forward.
2. Doublecurve; curve up.
3. Retrace; curve right.

School Home

144

Stop and Check

Circle your best *G*.

Circle S and $\mathscr{S}$ in these words.

Sam joined the chorus.

Trace and write.

$\mathscr{S}$ $\mathscr{S}$ $\mathscr{S}$ $\mathscr{S}$ $\mathscr{S}$ $\mathscr{S}$ $\mathscr{S}$

$\mathscr{S}$ is not joined to the letter that follows. Write words that begin with $\mathscr{S}$. Write the sentence.

Saturday   *Sunday*

Sam loves to sing.

Stroke description to guide letter formation at home:
1. Undercurve; loop; curve down and up.
2. Retrace; curve right.

Shape
Circle your best letter that has a loop.

145

Circle L and $\mathcal{L}$ in these words.

Lily made lemon tarts.

Lily made lemon tarts.

Trace and write.

$\mathcal{L}$ $\mathcal{L}$ $\mathcal{L}$ $\mathcal{L}$ $\mathcal{L}$ $\mathcal{L}$ $\mathcal{L}$ $\mathcal{L}$ $\mathcal{L}$

$\mathcal{L}$ is not joined to the letter that follows. Write words that begin with $\mathcal{L}$. Write the sentence.

Lucas   Lacey   Logan

Lily shares her dessert.

Stroke description to guide letter formation at home:

I. Undercurve; loop; curve down; loop; curve under.

Stop and Check
Circle your best $\mathcal{L}$.

Circle P and $\mathcal{P}$ in these words.

Put your books away.

Put your books away.

Trace and write.

$\mathcal{P}$ $\mathcal{P}$ $\mathcal{P}$ $\mathcal{P}$ $\mathcal{P}$ $\mathcal{P}$ $\mathcal{P}$

$\mathcal{P}$ is not joined to the letter that follows. Write words that begin with $\mathcal{P}$. Write the sentence.

Patrick   Pam   Peyton

Play time is now!

Stroke description to guide letter formation at home:

1. Undercurve.
2. Slant.
3. Retrace; curve forward and back.

Size

Circle your best tall letter.

147

Circle R and $\mathcal{R}$ in these words.

Rick ate a rice cake.

Rick ate a rice cake.

Trace and write.

 $\mathcal{R}$ $\mathcal{R}$ $\mathcal{R}$ $\mathcal{R}$ $\mathcal{R}$ $\mathcal{R}$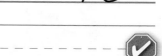

$\mathcal{R}$ is joined to the letter that follows. Write words that begin with $\mathcal{R}$. Write the sentence.

Rosita   *Ryan*   *Riley*

Rick ate grapes, too.

Stroke description to guide letter formation at home:

1. Undercurve.
2. Slant.
3. Retrace; curve forward and back.
4. Curve forward; undercurve.

Stop and Check
Circle your best $\mathcal{R}$.

Circle B and $\mathcal{B}$ in these words.

Bingo buries a bone.

Bingo buries a bone.

Trace and write.

$\mathcal{B}$ $\mathcal{B}$ $\mathcal{B}$ $\mathcal{B}$ $\mathcal{B}$ $\mathcal{B}$

$\mathcal{B}$ is not joined to the letter that follows. Write words that begin with $\mathcal{B}$. Write the sentence.

Brandon Blanca Ben

Bobby plays with Bingo.

Stroke description to guide letter formation at home:

1. Undercurve.
2. Slant.
3. Retrace; curve forward; loop; curve forward and back.
4. Retrace; curve right.

Spacing

Circle your best joining.

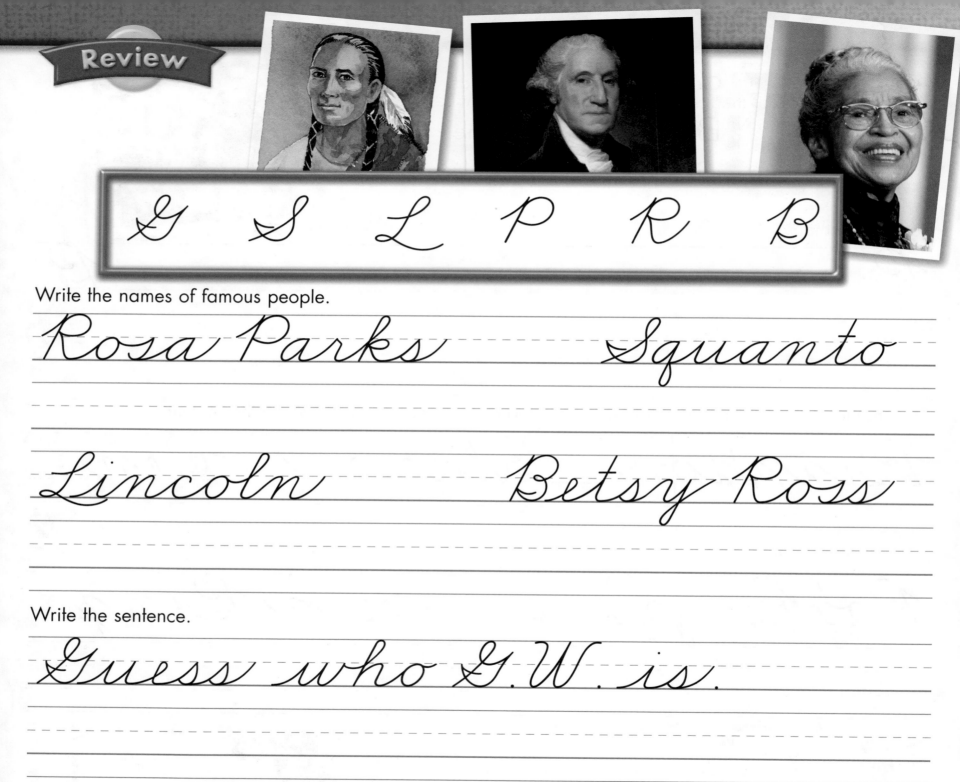

G   S   L   P   R   B

Write the names of famous people.

Rosa Parks   Squanto

Lincoln   Betsy Ross

Write the sentence.

Guess who G.W. is.

Choose one or two of the following famous firsts, and write them in cursive on the guidelines below.

1789: George Washington is first U.S. president.
1849: Elizabeth Blackwell is first American woman doctor.
1927: Charles Lindbergh is first to fly solo across Atlantic Ocean.
1983: Sally Ride is first American woman in space.
2009: Barack Obama is first African American U.S. president.

Shape Circle your best letter that has an overcurve stroke.
Size Circle your best tall letter.
Spacing Circle a word you wrote that has good spacing.
Slant Circle a word you wrote that has good slant.

Keys to Legibility

Slant

Spacing

Size

Shape

Write the following thank-you letter on the guidelines below.

Make your writing easy to read. Be sure to leave space for margins.

Dear Mr. and Mrs. Pool,
Thank you for the book.
I really like it. My sister
does, too! Thank you again.
Sincerely,
Jake

Write a thank-you letter to someone who did something nice for you.
Be sure to leave space for margins. Indent the first line of the paragraph.

Is your writing easy to read?

Shape
Circle your best letter that has an overcurve beginning.

Size
Circle your best short letter.

Spacing
Circle two words that have space for \ between them.

Slant
Circle a letter you wrote that has good slant.

Uppercase Cursive Review

Write the name for each letter of the alphabet in your best cursive handwriting.

Alyssa   Beth   Charles

Daniel   Emma   Felipe

Gabe   Hunter   Isabel

Joe   Kim   Leah   Max

Natalie   Omar   Pablo

Quentin   Rob   Sarah

Tyler   Ursula   Victor

Wade   Xander   Yasmin

Zachary

My writing has good **Shape** ☐
My writing has good **Size** ☐
My writing has good **Spacing** ☐
My writing has good **Slant** ☐

Show What You Can Do

City
In the morning the city
Spreads its wings
Making a song
In stone that sings.

Write the title and the first four lines of the poem in your best cursive handwriting.

In the evening the city
Goes to bed
Hanging lights
About its head.

by Langston Hughes

Write the next four lines here.

_____

- - - - - - - - - - - - - - - - - - -

_____

_____

- - - - - - - - - - - - - - - - - - -

_____

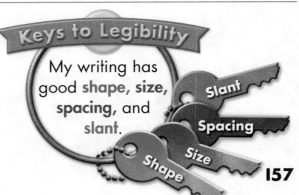

Keys to Legibility

My writing has good **shape, size, spacing,** and **slant**.

Slant

Spacing

Size

Shape

157

The Purple Cow

I never saw a purple cow,
I never hope to see one;
But I can tell you, anyhow,
I'd rather see than be one.

Gelett Burgess

Writing a Paragraph

Write the paragraph about the Fourth of July holiday. Be sure to leave space for margins. Indent the first line of the paragraph.

We marched in our town's July Fourth parade this year. Mom got to carry the big American flag! The newspaper had a picture of her. Her name was even in the first sentence of the article. In the evening we had a big picnic dinner. Later, we watched the fireworks over Lake Michigan.

Writing Quickly

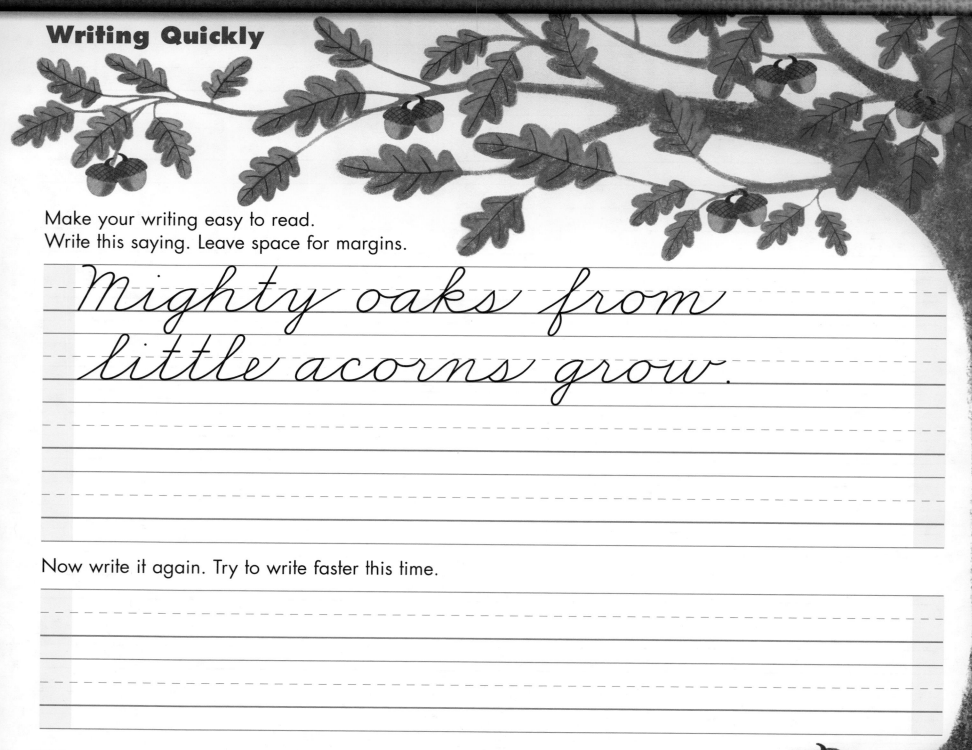

Make your writing easy to read.
Write this saying. Leave space for margins.

Mighty oaks from little acorns grow.

Now write it again. Try to write faster this time.

Write the saying again. Try to write even faster.
Make sure your writing is easy to read.

Now read your writing. Ask others to read it, too.
Then circle Yes or No next to each sentence.

My writing is easy for me to read.   Yes   No

My writing is easy for others to read.   Yes   No

Writing Easily

When your writing flows easily, you don't have to worry about your handwriting. You can just think about what you want to say.

Read the writing prompt below. Write your story on the lines. Let your handwriting flow easily. Remember to leave space for margins and indent the first line of each paragraph.

Narrative Writing

Write a story about what you see in the picture. Tell what might happen next.

Now read your final writing. Circle Yes or No to respond to each statement.
Then show your writing to another reader, either a classmate or your teacher.
Ask that person to circle Yes or No beside each statement.

	My Evaluation	My Classmate's or Teacher's Evaluation
The writing is easy to read.	Yes No	Yes No
The writing has good Shape.	Yes No	Yes No
The writing has good Size.	Yes No	Yes No
The writing has good Spacing.	Yes No	Yes No
The writing has good Slant.	Yes No	Yes No

Handwriting and the Writing Process

Write about a special place you visited. Tell what you saw there.
Write on a piece of writing paper. Follow these five steps as you write.

1. Prewriting

Plan ideas for your writing.
Use good handwriting so you can
read your ideas later.

2. Drafting

Write your ideas in sentences.
Your writing should be easy to read.

3. Revising

Revise your writing.
Make changes so that it says what you mean.

4. Editing

Check your spelling, punctuation, and handwriting.
Make sure your writing is easy to read.

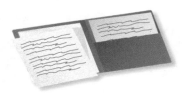

5. Publishing

Share your writing with others.
Use your best handwriting.

Record of Student's Handwriting Skills

Manuscript/*Cursive*

	Needs Improvement	Shows Mastery
Positions paper correctly for manuscript writing	☐	☐
Holds pencil correctly	☐	☐
Writes vertical lines	☐	☐
Writes horizontal lines	☐	☐
Writes circle lines	☐	☐
Writes slant lines	☐	☐
Writes manuscript **lL, iI**	☐	☐
Writes manuscript **tT, oO**	☐	☐
Writes manuscript **aA, dD**	☐	☐
Writes manuscript **cC, eE**	☐	☐
Writes manuscript **fF, gG**	☐	☐
Writes manuscript **jJ, qQ**	☐	☐
Writes manuscript **uU, sS**	☐	☐
Writes manuscript **bB, pP**	☐	☐
Writes manuscript **rR, nN**	☐	☐
Writes manuscript **mM, hH**	☐	☐
Writes manuscript **vV, yY**	☐	☐
Writes manuscript **wW, xX**	☐	☐
Writes manuscript **kK, zZ**	☐	☐
Writes manuscript numerals **1–10**	☐	☐

	Needs Improvement	Shows Mastery
Positions paper correctly for cursive writing	☐	☐
Writes undercurve strokes	☐	☐
Writes downcurve strokes	☐	☐
Writes overcurve strokes	☐	☐
Writes slant strokes	☐	☐
Writes cursive *i, t, u, w, e, l, b*	☐	☐
Writes cursive *h, f, k, r, s, j, p*	☐	☐
Writes cursive *a, d, g, o, c, q*	☐	☐
Writes cursive *n, m, y, x, v, z*	☐	☐
Writes cursive *A, O, D, C, E*	☐	☐
Writes cursive *N, M, H, K, U*	☐	☐
Writes cursive *Y, Z, V, W, X*	☐	☐
Writes cursive *I, J, Q, T, F*	☐	☐
Writes cursive *G, S, L, P, R, B*	☐	☐
Writes cursive numerals *1–10*	☐	☐
Writes with correct shape	☐	☐
Writes with correct size	☐	☐
Writes with correct spacing	☐	☐
Writes with correct slant	☐	☐
Regularly checks written work for legibility	☐	☐

Index